WESTERN KENT

Edited by Lynsey Hawkins

First published in Great Britain in 2003 by
YOUNG WRITERS
Remus House,
Coltsfoot Drive,
Peterborough, PE2 9JX
Telephone (01733) 890066

HB ISBN 1 84460 142 0
SB ISBN 1 84460 143 9

FOREWORD

Young Writers was established in 1991 as a
foundation for promoting the reading and writing of
poetry amongst children and young adults. Today it
continues this quest and proceeds to nurture and guide
the writing talents of today's youth.

From this year's competition Young Writers is proud
to present a showcase of the best poetic talent from
across the UK. Each hand-picked poem has been
carefully chosen from over 66,000 'Hullabaloo!'
entries to be published in this, our eleventh primary
school series.

This year in particular we have been wholeheartedly
impressed with the quality of entries received. The
thought, effort, imagination and hard work put into
each poem impressed us all and once again the task of
editing was a difficult but enjoyable experience.

We hope you are as pleased as we are with the final
selection and that you and your family will continue
to be entertained with *Hullabaloo! Western Kent* for
many years to come.

CONTENTS

The Poems

PARENTS

Oh heck, them, *no,*
I don't need reminding.
But of course, where would
We be without them?

Still

Do this! Do that!
Tidy your room!
Take out the trash!
Is there no end?

And

Shovel the walk!
Turn off that TV!
You've left the light on!
Please!

But

I can't wait till I can leave home,
I can do what I like,
I can drive, I can blow my money
But for some reason they are special to me.

Adrian Register (11)
Hildenborough CE Primary School

AFRICAN

My hands that labour,
My feet that drag,
My eyes that squint,
My legs that lag.

My brain confused,
My eardrums burst,
My spine that's crushed,
My mouth that's cursed.

My heart that pounds,
My hair uncombed,
My cheeks of red,
My eyes untoned.

My teeth of yellow,
My nails of black,
My stomach empty,
Water I lack.

Emma Richardson (10)
Hildenborough CE Primary School

MOONLIT NIGHT

At night I sit up and look at the stars
Looking and listening
I hear the hoot of an owl
I hear the rustling of mice
The wind blows gently
The trees sway slightly
There is a howl of a dog and a miaow of a cat
As it goes hunting into the night
Tonight a full moon shines brightly
Suddenly a dark cloud appears and blocks out the moon
I'm plunged into darkness
There's another hoot and a chink of glass
As I hear the grown-ups talking downstairs
A cool breeze skims my face and ruffles my hair
The clouds move away
The moon shines down on me
I leave a gap in the curtains to look at the moon
I get back into bed
The stars twinkle down at me
I close my eyes and drift silently off to sleep.

Lydia Marsh (10)
Hildenborough CE Primary School

RISE AND SHINE!

Hot steamy porridge
Bubbling on the cooker
Covered in sugar and spice
Oh, it does look nice
Will it warm my tummy?
Umm it's really yummy.

      'Hurry, hurry,' I hear Mum say,
      'Or you'll be late again today
      Brush your teeth and comb your hair
      Make your bed and go downstairs
      Grab your coat, jump in the car
      Off we go, it's not too far!'

In the car park
I hear the bell
Phew, just in time for
Show-and-tell!

Brittany Etherington (11)
Hildenborough CE Primary School

KINGFISHER

When you see the dazzling blue,
Or the bright hot orange
Darting along the river bank and then
It dives into a stream.
You immediately think, *kingfisher.*

It dives like an arrow before
Hitting its target.
Not a moment too soon
Straight into the bull's-eye.
He flies onto a perch with a waiting female.

He turns the fish around
In its dagger-like beak.
The female takes the fish
And swallows it whole.
The courtship is now complete.

Then as quick as a flash
The male jumps right onto her back
Holds on to her brilliant crown feathers.
Then the mating is complete.

Then she lays an egg, a little like an oval face.
Then there is a rumble like a tummy rumbling.
Then there is a tapping sound
And then there is a crack.
Out comes the beak
Then comes the head
Then the tiny wings
And a thin body, tiny legs and feet.

David Flack (10)
Hildenborough CE Primary School

A MAN CALLED PRESTON

There once was a man called Preston
Who always used to have something to rest on
I'm not saying he's big
But he eats like a pig
And now he's got indigestion!

His first name was Jim
And he wants to be slim
So he looks at himself
With a mirror on the shelf
And now he goes to the gym!

Alfie Hall (11)
Hildenborough CE Primary School

SEASONS

If you place into your hand
Snow on grass
Dew and ice
You will be holding winter

If you place into your hand
A beautiful sunset
And a lamb
You will be holding spring

If you place into your hand
A ball of burning fire
And the laughter of children
You will be holding summer

If you place into your hand
The trees without their leaves
And the sun without its gleam
You will be holding autumn.

Hannah Thompson (10)
Hildenborough CE Primary School

MY TEDDY

My teddy, he's seen better days,
But I love him so.
Every time I look at him,
I feel a red-hot glow.

He's there when I need him,
When the day's been rough,
His presence seems to give me strength,
'I'll get through, however tough!'

He's there every evening,
When I get home from school,
Even just his sweet little face,
Seems to help me keep my cool.

He's there to snuggle up to in bed,
On cold winter nights,
His furry body keeps me secure,
From any night-time frights.

My teddy, he means the world to me,
He's mine and it'll stay that way,
He'll stay with me my whole life through,
Until I pass away.

Abigail Hinton (10)
Hildenborough CE Primary School

THE ARRIVAL OF WINTER

Winter is coming,
Summer is going.
Down goes the summer sun.
The fun-filled days are old and gone.

Animals hibernate,
Birds start to migrate.
Hedgehogs sleep,
Down comes the sleet.

Geese say goodbye
To warmer lands, off they fly.
Leaves coming off the trees,
The lakes are cold, soon they will freeze.

The days are short, the nights are long,
A robin starts to sing his song.
Christmas will soon be near,
The air shall be full of festive cheer.

The trees are bare, they have no leaves,
Disappeared have the bees.
Don't go outside without knowing,
Whether or not it is snowing!

Bethany Surgenor (11)
Hildenborough CE Primary School

AUTUMN SENSES

Smell the misty foggy air
Thick with the sweet scents
Of the autumn flowers
Smell the freshly cut grass
All neat and trim
Smell the icy rain
Beating down through the tropical air
Slicing through the heat
Smell the scents of autumn.

See the emerald-green leaves
Turning to burgundy and brown
See the leaves twisting, turning
Falling to the ground, nearly dead
See their last minute of life
As they flicker like an almost dead bulb
See the green shoots
Turning brown as they die
See the sights of autumn.

Hear the crunching of the leaves
As Bigfoot takes his stride
Hear the breaking of the twigs
As they die and fall to the ground
Hear the threatening wind
Like a whistling hurricane
Hear the golden leaves
Being ripped off the old branches
Hear the sound of autumn.

Jenny Nevard (11)
Hildenborough CE Primary School

THE FOUR SEASONS

The year starts off with spring
As the birds come out and sing.
As dormice stare with sleepy eyes
Other animals come out in surprise.

The buds appear on trees
And form very small leaves.
As flowers break the soil
Gardeners prepare to toil.

Summer has begun
Now is the time to have fun!
Playing water fights
And having loads of delights.

We all like to sunbathe
But sometimes we want the shade of a cave.
Leaves start to die
Goodbye sunny sky!

Autumn fills the trees
With red, gold and brown leaves.
Winter is almost here
Now is the time for good cheer!

The year is at its end
Now is the time to spend!
Soon we will have some snow
But eventually it will have to go!

These are the four seasons of the year
So go out - don't be stuck in here!
You could have lots of fun
In the snow or the sun!

George Lipington (11)
Hildenborough CE Primary School

WINTER FEELINGS

The cold winds blow,
Snow falls, wet and cold,
Streets become icy overnight,
Gritters wander up and down the streets,
Winter's coming cold and sharp.

Children make snowmen and wrap up warm,
Frozen ponds become ice rinks full of happiness,
Streets become caught up in snowball fights,
Houses warm and cosy wait for children cold and wet,
Winter's here warm and cosy.

Central heating put on full,
Children hanging up their stockings waiting for Santa,
Dreams of toys and presents filling their heads,
Happy faces fill the air, toys and presents everywhere,
Winter, the season with loves and hates.

Bethan Hull (10)
Hildenborough CE Primary School

SCHOOL

Somewhere to learn,
Somewhere to play,
Somewhere to look forward,
To the end of the day.

Typing on computers,
Working in your books,
Chatting in the corner,
Getting dirty looks.

Literacy and numeracy,
Geography and art,
Or even after school clubs,
I love taking part.

I enjoy playing netball,
Shooting for our team,
I'm proud to wear the uniform,
I keep it nice and clean.

Hildenborough teachers
Are the very best,
Bet they can't wait for me to leave,
So they can have a *rest!*

Robyn Simmons (11)
Hildenborough CE Primary School

SUNDAY MORNING

It's Sunday morning
So wet and muddy,
As I fly across the field.

Once again
He's taken down,
Hurrah, hurrah for us.

As quick as a flash
We charge,
Aaaggghhh!

A string of passes led to me
I dived, I dived,
I scored the winning try.

Hurrah, hurrah
We've won the match,
We've won the match, oh yes!

From tackles to passes
It all felt good,
Especially the win!

Boohoo, boohoo
It is all over,
It is all over and now forgotten.

Jack Mutch (11)
Hildenborough CE Primary School

WINTER

Frozen lakes
Snow that falls
Icy roads
Droplet jewels.

Morning dew
Birds that sing
Winter's breath
On everything!

Cold outside
In the snow
Frozen leaves
Temperatures low.

Snowball fights
In the streets
Hats and gloves
Nice warm treats.

Joanie Eaton (10)
Hildenborough CE Primary School

ANGER/LOVE

Anger

Anger is a hungry devil sucking
The emotions from your heart.
Anger is like a red-hot fire,
The more logs you put the more wild it gets.
Anger is a feeling of heartburn
Giving extreme pain.
Anger is like a hot, spicy, red sauce
That makes your mouth sizzle and burn.
Anger is like red, exploding fireworks.
Keep away from the *red-hot devil!*

Love

Love is a sweet melody singing
Through your heart.
Love is like meditation - peaceful, quiet and romantic.
Love is soft as spread cheese
Love is ice cream cooling you down.
Love is like a rainbow - settling and calm
Love is the best thing
That can happen to you!

Sapna Marwaha (10)
Hildenborough CE Primary School

ANGER

Anger is the colour of a deep fiery red,
Orange, yellow flames.
Anger feels hot, burns inside my head,
It's giving me such terrible pain.
Anger tastes hot, like a spicy curry,
Burning my delicate tongue.
Anger smells strong, it smells of worry,
Hating everyone.
Anger looks like a fire with a flickering flame,
Burning in front of my eyes.
Anger sounds like the destruction of a crashing plane
And one thousand million lies.
Anger is the worst there is,
Out of sadness, happiness or stress.
Anger gets you into quite a tizz,
It's the worst emotion to possess.

Gemma Johnson (11)
Hildenborough CE Primary School

BROTHERS

I'm part of a family of six,
We get up to all sorts of tricks.
My mum and my dad are old and quite sad,
And me and my brothers don't mix.

My brothers total three
And all of them bigger you see.
They're called Hamish, Charlie and Chris
And each of them dominate me.

With Charlie I have to be brave.
He thinks I am his slave.
He's the oldest this one, the number one son
And doesn't know how to behave

My second problem is Chris,
He's not too nice to his sis.
On the PlayStation 2 he says, 'Better than you.'
His hair is a bit of a miss.

They all think Hamish is a saint,
My favourite he definitely ain't.
It is impossible to rhyme with his name
And trying to has made me insane!

Eleanor de Rusett (10)
Hildenborough CE Primary School

BLACK

Black is the deep darkness of the night
Black is a place concealed from light
Black is a bat's velvet fur
Black is a spider beginning to stir

Black is the monster under the bed
Black is all the things that you dread
Black is the heart of all demons alike
Black is the creatures that stir in the night.

Gemma Corden (11)
Hildenborough CE Primary School

THE SEASONS ARE HERE

Spring is here,
Flowers grow,
New buds sprout
And rivers flow.

Summer is here,
The sun is shining,
Golden-red it still will glow,
The heat is rising.

Autumn is here,
The leaves are falling,
Falling from the autumn trees,
Flowers are dying.

Winter is here,
The snow is falling,
Icicles hanging on garden sheds,
Animals hibernating.

Aliza Goren (10)
Hildenborough CE Primary School

IF I WERE RICH

If I were rich I think I'd buy . . .
A swimming pool complete with slides,
A theme park packed with loads of rides.
I'd donate money to the poor,
Buy a house by the seashore,
Create a library just for me,
A golden beach with a clear blue sea,
A telescope to see the stars,
Jupiter, the moon and Mars,
A robot to clean up my room,
A flashy car that goes *vroom vroom.*
Sadly, none of this can be
Until we win the lottery!

Amelia Stepto (10)
Hildenborough CE Primary School

FEELINGS

Love

Love is the colour of pink.
It feels like the best sensation ever is being swept over you.
It tastes like champagne and chocolates.
It looks like children playing and having fun.
It sounds like children laughing and birds singing happily together.
It smells like a red rose.
Love is a brilliant feeling.

Anger

Anger is dark red.
It feels like you are being stabbed in the heart.
It tastes bitter.
It looks like people fighting with one another.
It sounds like a shrill, cold, empty scream.
It smells like a dead rotting animal.
Anger is a horrible feeling to have.

Happiness

Happiness is the colour of bright yellow.
It feels like you are flying away from your worries.
It tastes like fruit picked freshly off trees on a tropical island.
It looks like long-lost friends meeting again.
It sounds like people chatting with their friends.
It smells like apple pie freshly baked.
Happiness is a wonderful feeling to have.

Jealousy

Jealousy is the colour of green.
It feels like you want to do something awful.
It tastes like dry bread and water.
It looks like everybody having fun except for you.
It sounds like a nothingness silence.
It smells like cheese that has gone off.
Jealousy is an awful feeling to have.

Kindness

Kindness is the colour of light blue.
It feels like something nice you have done to someone else
Has made you feel great.
It tastes like chocolate cake.
It looks like friends playing happily with one another.
It sounds like a sweet harmony being sung to you.
It smells like flowers freshly picked.
Kindness is one of the best feelings to have.

Sadness

Sadness is the colour of dark blue.
It feels like nobody loves you.
It tastes like rotting fish.
It looks like all your friends are playing but leaving you out.
It sounds like a sad humming in your ear that never goes away.
It smells like an old damp towel.
Sadness is a horrible feeling to have.

Tabitha Longley-Coomber (10)
Hildenborough CE Primary School

IF I RULED THE WORLD...

If I ruled the world . . .
Children would teach teachers,
Teach them important lessons,
Like football and how to have fun.

If I ruled the world . . .
People would be in the cages,
While animals walked around and stared,
Licking ice lollies.

If I ruled the world . . .
There would be free entry to Center Parcs,
Just for kids, no grown-ups allowed.
Ah, if I ruled the world . . .

But I've only got 50p!

Elise Evans (10)
Hildenborough CE Primary School

THE HARE

Quick, dash,
Slick, flash,
There goes the hare.
Running fast,
Never last,
There goes the hare.
Long and lean,
Only a glimpse ever seen.
There goes the hare.

Down comes the eagle, like a spear through the sky.
Run, hare, run, if he gets you it's over with your fun.
The hare races fast, the eagle swoops low
And with one massive claw, he gives the final blow.

Alex Mortlock (11)
Hildenborough CE Primary School

STORY TIME

'Right class 3! *I said right class 3!*
I will read you a story if you behave.
Alright? So. Once upon a time - yes Gavin?
Yes, you can go to the toilet Gavin, but be quick.
No Gavin, you needn't be faster than the speed of light,
You can just be quick. So.
Once upon a time there was *Susan!*
You do *not* punch Rachel. No, not even if
She stuck her tongue out at you.
Leave each other alone.
Once upon a time there was
A beautiful princess called - yes Gavin?
No Gavin, you *can't* go to the toilet again.
Harry - what did I say about picking your nose?
Don't do it. It's not nice.
Now, this princess was called Cinderella -
Good afternoon Mrs Rowley,
That would be nice, but I'm busy at the moment,
Later, yes, later.
Don't be upset, I think that is really good.
Goodbye. *Goodbye.*
Right. Here goes
OnceuponatimetherewasaprincesscalledCinderella
Shehadareallykindfather. Yes Janet?
No, I don't know if she had any pets.
Oh! There is the bell.
What a *shame!*'

Madeleine Tuz (10)
Hildenborough CE Primary School

HUNTED

You run like the wind and across the plain,
Kicking up dust you'll never see again.

Your eyes are fixed forward, never look back,
Trying to go gently so they don't see your tracks.

Your ears are pricked up, your nose pointing down,
Running like hell over dry dusty ground.

Your legs have gone wild through fear alone,
If they catch you they'll kill you and pull you from bone.

A spear whistles past you and you're terrified,
Another on your left and in the blink of an eye,
You're on the floor and you're going to die.

Your life flashes before you and you know it's the end,
Your wounds are fatal that no one can mend.

Your blood trickles from you, it's all over the ground
And your heart stops its beating, it no longer does pound.

Bethany Crouch (11)
Hildenborough CE Primary School

WINTER IS HERE

W inter is here
I   cy winds blow
N o leaves on the trees
T he roads blocked with snow
E ngines rumble as cars skid
R aging cold temperatures are so livid.

I   cicles falling off the roofs
S eeing horses, cold are their hooves.

H ail and snow
E verywhere you go
R ain, thunder and lightning
E verything is frightening.

Ben Richards (11)
Hildenborough CE Primary School

WHEN I DREAM

When I dream,
It's a wonderful thing,
There are really nice bees,
That never ever sting.

There're flowers that talk,
Magic carpets too,
There's no school at all
And for all the exams you always get through.

There're horses with wings,
Who float around in the sky,
There're loads of different types of food,
My favourite's apple pie.

When they say goodbye,
I feel a bit sad,
But they reassure me that I can come back soon,
So it makes me feel oh so glad.

Alissa Stroud (9)
Hilden Oaks School

HOMEWORK

Writing English poems
Or doing lots of sums
I really do hate homework
And so do dads and mums

They always try to help me
But they're never any good
Even my brother Chris can't help
And he's in year 11 at Judd

My brother Greg's at Hilden Grange
And he gets more than me,
He spends all evening doing it
And doesn't even stop for tea.

I suppose I'll have to concentrate
And work it out alone,
Or maybe I can phone a friend.
Is that Emma on the phone?

Now that's homework done,
I can have a rest,
At least I've worked as hard as I can,
I think I've done my best.

Annalise Byrne (9)
Hilden Oaks School

HAIR

Good hair
Long, silky, golden hair
Blonde, shiny hair
Brown, newly-washed hair
Red, curly hair
Fair hair

Bad hair
Short, greasy, black hair
Silver streaked hair
Green and blue dyed hair
Spiky, wet, red hair
Yellow glow in the dark hair.

Grace Curds (11)
Hilden Oaks School

BEST FRIENDS

Someone who cares
Someone who shares
A person to talk to
Who is always there for you
A friend who makes you happy
When you are feeling sad
Who makes you laugh
When you are really mad
Sometimes you don't agree with them
And both of you fall out
But then you both say sorry
'We are friends again!' we shout.
Will a best friend let you down? *Never!*
Best friends are forever.

Katie Hayward (10)
Hilden Oaks School

CATS

My two cats are cute,
Their names are Cindy and Smudge.
In the morning they play
Then eat their food

After that they play again
When the door opens
Off they go
To play in the garden until four o'clock
Then they come in to eat their tea
And then it's off to bed
Those two little sleepyheads!

Hayley Musson (10)
Hilden Oaks School

MY SPRINGER SPANIEL

My springer spaniel is cheeky, naughty too.
Yesterday she bit the next-door neighbour's shoe.
Every day she always gets muddy.
She runs into the study and makes a mess.
But the best thing about her is she's loving and cuddly.
That's my dog Molly.

Fenella Green (9)
Hilden Oaks School

WHAT ARE YOU DOING TOMORROW?

Somehow I seem to be doing a number of things,
There's collecting prizes from various kings.
There is one in Majorca and one in LA
I think I'm going to have a busy day.

Well I'm sailing across the Atlantic
And then meeting the Queen,
Then there is climbing Kilamanjaro
And eating a huge ice cream.
My day's the busiest you have ever seen.

I'm competing in the Olympics
I hope to win and impress.
If I am at my best they'll surely call in the press.
My day is so busy they should make me a princess.

I'm appearing on Blue Peter with Lizz, Connie and Matt.
How could your day be busier than that?

I am swimming with dolphins
I'm sure it will be divine.
Just how could your day be busier than mine?

'I am not doing anything much,
Just going to see my mum.
But I will tell you something
My day is going to be fun!'

Amy Roberts (11)
Hilden Oaks School

RAINDROPS

Rain falling
Pittering, pattering
Children cringing
Tears running
Pitter-patter, pitter-patter
On the roof
Dogs howling
Glistening, shimmering
Raindrops dancing
Falling ruling
Colourful rainbows in the sky
Woof, woof, woof.

Felicity Forster (10)
Hilden Oaks School

WHAT TO WRITE?

I like writing poems but what to say?
How about what a lovely day?
No, that doesn't sound right
Oh dear, oh dear what to write?
I look at the girl sitting next to me
I counted her lines, she did twenty-three
I wish I could write poems that well
But I'm just rubbish, can't you tell?

Rachel Jackson (9)
Hilden Oaks School

SCHOOL DINNERS

School dinners, what are they like?
Disgusting, disgusting, disgusting!
Soggy broccoli, mushy peas and cold baked beans,
Fatty meat - thank goodness I'm a veggie.

I wish they could be better,
Only lukewarm water to drink,
Why can't we have a packed lunch?
That would be so much more tasty.

Egg and cress sandwiches, crisps,
I'm drooling at the thought,
Strawberries dipped in chocolate,
Wouldn't that be scrumptious?

Ice-cold jugs of fizzy drinks,
Ben and Jerry's ice cream
And After Eight mints,
Now that's what I call school dinners!

Grace Carpenter (9)
Hilden Oaks School

SCHOOL

School is sometimes cool
But sometimes I hate school
Maths is OK
But English is *no* way

PE is the best
The bad thing is a test
Play time is fun
You get to run

Fish and chips are nice
I hate the school rice
Homework is boring
Indoor play is when it is pouring

If you leave things on the floor
You have to pay more
If you are sad
Your friends cheer you up by going mad.

Victoria Bishop (9) & Laura Pope (10)
Hilden Oaks School

TRYING TO WRITE A POEM

I can't think
I can't do it
I can't find a rhyme
I hate writing poetry, it takes up so much time

I can't find a subject
I can't find a theme
I can't find my copy book
Mum thinks I'm in a dream

Wait a moment I can find a subject
I can find a theme
I've just written a poem
And I'm not in a daydream.

Emily McEachern (9)
Hilden Oaks School

A SCHOOLBOY RHYME

In our class there is a boy
A boy who likes to rhyme,
One day the teacher gasped and cried,
'Oh my Lord it's almost time!'

She said this with a ghastly tone,
A ghastly tone to chill the bone,
Because you see she won't deny,
How she hates the boy's rhymes.

She packed her bags and off she went,
Towards the classroom door,
Until she heard the pattering footsteps,
Of feet upon the floor.

Then in stepped the rhyming boy
With the rest of his class,
The teacher knew what was coming
And then with a blast . . .

'Teacher, teacher, teacher
Let me tell you what I just saw,
I saw a woman just like you,
Escape from school this morn.

Teacher . . . where are you?'

Jacobina Donald (10)
Hilden Oaks School

THE PLAYGROUND

As the girls dance and sing,
The boys make paper aeroplanes and things,
The teachers make sure things are okay,
While the children happily play,
As the girls play clapping games,
The boys shout out names,
The teachers help when children are ill,
Then children go to the nurse and take a pill,
As they have fun the day goes fast
And teachers send them back to class,
Sadly then children stop their songs
And can't wait till next play time comes along.

Emma Brown (10)
Hilden Oaks School

WORDS

Words can be of happiness or sadness,
They can open your heart and fill you with gladness.

Words from my father when I've been bad
Can make me feel horrible and really, really sad.

Words from my teacher go on and on,
Especially when I get all my spellings wrong!

Words from my mother when there's chores to do,
Are not very cheerful, I'm telling you!

Words from my friend, about the latest fashions,
Really seem to suit all of my passions.

Words from Pru when we're deciding what to play,
Get us in a lot of trouble, at the end of the day.

Rebecca Moore (10)
Hilden Oaks School

THE SOUND IN THE NIGHT

There was a sound in the night,
That gave me a fright,
It ran through my very skin.
It was monstrous and loud,
Petrifying and proud
And gave an awful din.

There was a sound in the night,
That didn't sound right,
I started to feel uneasy.
It made me shiver,
It made me quiver
And I started to feel rather queasy.

There was a sound in the night,
As the moon shone bright,
That was the scariest I've ever known.
It was deep and low
And seemed to grow,
It chilled me right to the bone.

There was a sound in the night,
I heard it all right,
It was coming from something I could see.
It was horse deep grunting
Like people hunting
And it was coming from a terrifying tree.

Rebecca Phelps (9)
Hilden Oaks School

POWERPUFF GIRLS

With Blossom, Bubbles and Buttercup too,
Your favourite colours are green, pink and blue.
Rushing around at the speed of light,
Come on girls fight, fight, fight.

Whoosh, sparkle, punch, pow,
Kill Mo-jo-jo-jo, quickly, now.
Go girls don't give him a chance,
Go give him a merry dance.

The professor gives you lots of support,
The mayor has lots of things to report.
Miss Bellum she is very pretty
And Bubbles wants a sweet little kitty.

Kimberley Foster-Powell (10)
Hilden Oaks School

THE LION

The lion's *mane* is as gold as sand on a beach,
His *claws* are as sharp as a knife in a drawer,
His *roar* is as loud as *thunder!* in the night sky
And his *eyes* are as scary as lava
Shooting out of a volcano!

Elliot Harris (9)
Mayplace Primary School

THE GREAT MOON

The moon is as bright as a diamond in the sky
It overtakes the whole planet
Never can anything be as bright as this crystal glittering
through the night.
When you see the moon at night
Just think of the wonderful things that happen and go on and on.

Jessica Williams (8)
Mayplace Primary School

THE SUN

The sun is like a dazzling sparkling gold head,
A ginormous diamond floating in the sky,
Coming up in the morning.
The yellow is like the sand in the water,
The orange is like the sand out of the water,
The clouds are like big chunks of candyfloss.

Holly Green (9)
Mayplace Primary School

MY LION

My lion roars like thunderous thunder.
My lion has a tail of thick long rope.
My lion has a mane that never ends.
His coat is like a fleecy blanket because he is so soft.

Alice Woodland (8)
Mayplace Primary School

MY PUPPY BLUE

I have a little puppy
We call him Blue,
He loves to chew anything in sight,
Things like his toys and always my shoe.
He loves his walk which he has every night,
But sometimes gives people a fright.
He is such a lively puppy,
We love him so much,
People walking by always stop and say hi,
As he gets so excited if anyone passes by.

Connor Flaherty (8)
Mayplace Primary School

LOVE

Violets are blue, roses are red,
But our love will never ever separate.
Together forever, forever together,
Whether you like it or not.
Put your ring on my lonely finger,
Let our love flicker.
Violets are blue, roses are red,
But our love will never ever separate.
Together forever whether you like it or not.
My love for you is getting stronger
Than you will ever know,
I'll try and make it show.

Emmabelle Nwadikwa (7)
Mayplace Primary School

FAIRY FOLK

Come and sit by the fire,
Let me tell you about the fairy folk.
They fly on the golden fireflies
That scatter across the night skies.

At dawn they open the flowers,
By sprinkling their fairy dust across the meadows.
Even under the branches of trees,
To awaken the flowers in the shadows.

Lauran Allam (8)
Mayplace Primary School

TIME TO REFLECT

I am your double, if you break me
There'll be trouble.
I never lie, not even to a fly.
Please please don't break,
You'll be sure to cry.
Alice looked through it,
The wicked witch spoke to it,
Harry daydreamed through it.
I can see young, I can see old,
I can see magic.

Jack Whitehead (7)
Mayplace Primary School

I'M A BIG YELLOW DAISY

I'm a little daisy short and sweet
I dance in the meadow
I'm springy on my feet
I hide in long grass
And dance with the wind
I'm a big yellow daisy
That plays with my friends.

Robert Ware (7)
Mayplace Primary School

I AM

Animal - I am a pony because I like to gallop like a pony.
Colour - I am gold because I like to shine like gold.
Place - I am a hill because I like to be bumpy.
Food - I am pizza because I like to be spicy.
Feeling - I am happy because it is my birthday today.
Plant - I am a rose because I like the nice smells of them.
Weather - I am the sun because it is bright and warm.

Jenny Heselden (8)
Mayplace Primary School

I AM...

I am a gorilla because I stuff myself with food and like to bang
on my chest, *'Oooah!'*
I am invisible because I vanish in the day. *Cool!*
I am a sweet shop because I love eating these scrummy sweets.
I am black and I am proud.
I am a human being and one that is smart and has a kind heart.
I am a beauty and a beauty I am.
I am a person who picks their nose.
I am a lorry because when I'm at school
I always say, *'Beep, beep, broom, broom.'*
I am a poet and that's what I do.

Rayanne Ibrahim (7)
Mayplace Primary School

ME AND MY GOLDFISH

I love my goldfish,
My goldfish are blue,
My favourite food is fruit,
My favourite feeling is love,
My favourite place is home.

Lily Andrews (8)
Mayplace Primary School

I AM...

I am a fish because I like to swim very much.
I am green because I like the air and trees.
I am a museum because I like going to museums.
I am toast because I am warm.
I am happiness because I am cheerful.

Daniel Scanlon (8)
Mayplace Primary School

THE RIVER

The river is easily as fast as the fastest hound.
Sounds as loud as a lion's roar.
Glitters and gleams like diamonds in the sun
And its waters are filled with silvery fish.

Liam Rose (9)
Mayplace Primary School

THE SUN

The sun is like a football set on fire.
Racing through the sky
The sun is like an orange
That has got scorching flames,
Stuck up in the sky
The sun is like a lemon lollipop
The sun is a fireball
Hovering in the sky.

Thomas Steer (9)
Mayplace Primary School

WINTER

The trees shiver as he breathes down their necks,
The bushes crouch low, hoping not to be next,
The flowers get bullied
Until they shrivel up dead,
Birds are rushed roughly
Through his angry cold fists.

He strides through the streets
Threatening everyone he meets,
He'll pounce on you
So you'd better watch out,
For he is out there,
Scarier than mice!

To scare all your friends
All you have to do is this,
Shout out this sentence
With toughness and might,
Be ready, here it goes,
Please don't scream cos . . .
Winter is here!

Katherine Hockley (10)
Mayplace Primary School

I AM

Place: I am Africa because I am sunny and bright.
Feeling: I am cheerful because I am happy.
Colour: I am blue because it reminds me of the sky.
Animal: I am a bird so I can move swiftly through the sweet
summer air.

Thomas Styles (8)
Mayplace Primary School

THE LION

Growling a bolt of lightning strikes,
The lion growls so loud that even the trees
Shed their leaves.

Skin like a brand new teddy bear
All furry and soft!
Nose shiny and smooth as a button!

Eyes sly and narrow like a raindrop horizontally!
Tail long and thin like a rough rope
With wool on the tip of it!

Toni Oni (9)
Mayplace Primary School

THE SUN

The flaming burning bright sun
Floating in the sparkling sky
The golden sparks blazing out
Of the gleaming sun
It is shining on the new fresh grass
It looks like a diamond ring.

Lucy Browne (9)
Mayplace Primary School

THE LION

The lion fur is like birds' feathers in the air
As he walks his feet squelch in the mud
His tail is like crisps
In the wild, in the jungle
Raining and jumping.

Joshua Hammond (9)
Mayplace Primary School

THE MOON

The moon is a little gem in the sky,
It's slivery, glittery light twinkles
Down on the ground and on the darkest night.
When the moon's out the whole world lights up,
It looks like a gem so big, everything's white.

Sam Gibbons (9)
Mayplace Primary School

THE LION

The lion's roar is as loud as
A tenor horn on the moon
The ferocious lion has a mane like a bushy tail
His fur is corn glowing in the shimmering sunlight.

Ryan Stockley (8)
Mayplace Primary School

FLOWERS

Daffodils are scattered across the meadows far,
Whispering with excitement at every passing car,
They dance and they sway,
In their own unique way
And sing to their heart's content.

Roses are boasting, proud and vain,
Moaning as their petals get wet at every drop of rain,
'We are beautiful, we are tall,
Not like you at all,'
They cry to all the others.

Tulips are painting a pretty picture,
Just while standing in a colourful mixture,
With friends, places they swap,
Keeping up the beat of the bop,
Then they fall into the shape they want.

Yasmin Christy (10)
Mayplace Primary School

LION

Lion has a roar like thunder and lightning!
His mane is a thick jungle of hair.
He has eyes like spotlights in the distance.
He has a head that is harder than a cricket ball
And teeth like iron spikes!

Matthew Smith (9)
Mayplace Primary School

THE RIVER

The river is like a massive diamond
Laying on the ground.
The river is like a disco ball
Shining in the sky.
The river is like a stone
Floating in the ground.

Amy Maynard (9)
Mayplace Primary School

THE ROAD

The road is an elephant's skin,
Grey and smooth.
In the dark you have reflectors
That are elephants' eyes,
All glowing and gleaming
In the darkness.

Henna Jooma (9)
Mayplace Primary School

THE SUN

The sun is very, very powerful
Like a fireball
It's boiling hot
It's as clean as water
It is a refreshing yellow colour.

Chelsea Roberts (8)
Mayplace Primary School

LION

The lion roars like thunder.
His paws are like a sloth.
His strength is like a bear that's angry.
His tail is like a horse.
His temper is like a bull with a spear in its back,
But he knows he is king.

Matt Mowatt (9)
Mayplace Primary School

THE MOON

The moon is a five pence coin,
A silver cake
That hasn't been cut,
The craters on it
Are as grey as concrete,
The sky around it
Sucks in its light.

James Vallins (9)
Mayplace Primary School

THE MOON

The moon is as silver as a diamond on a ring,
Shiny like a pretty paperclip,
Shaped like a silver banana,
Glitters like a silver chalk
Way up in the sky!

Becky Downing (9)
Mayplace Primary School

RIVER

The river is a beautiful glowing diamond on the ground.
The river is like a shiny white colour and it gleams.
When the river is still it looks like a mirror.

Emma Harrison (9)
Mayplace Primary School

THE LION

Its growl is as loud as a strike of lightning,
Making the trees rumble,
Making the animals in the tree unconscious,
Having a mane of thick fur around its neck
And his teeth as sharp as blades
Going through your smooth silky skin.

Simon Moon (9)
Mayplace Primary School

THE LION

A lion must have a mane
Like a soft, comforting, furry rug.
It must have a tail with fur at the end
Flickering flames.
It must have tearing claws to catch prey
And sharp teeth to put prey to death
And devour it.

Ryan Fripps (9)
Mayplace Primary School

THE SUN

The sun is a gigantic round lemon,
A bitter lemon it is
Exploding with a vengeance of an ogre;
And the sky digests it
With its fluffy white sheep.

David Tighe-Ellis (8)
Mayplace Primary School

THE WITCH'S KITCHEN

In the witch's kitchen
There is a ragged broom blocking a dingy mouse hole
In the witch's kitchen
There is a black-winged cauldron bubbling away
In the witch's kitchen
There is a cat purring on the window sill
In the witch's kitchen
There is a glass case full of wands
In the witch's kitchen
There is a troll in a cage torturing children
In the witch's kitchen
There is a picture on the wall with eyes that follow you.

Jonathan Wing (9)
Normandy Primary School

DRUMS

Drums are noisy
Drums are sweet
Only if you can control the beat
Bing, bong, bing, bong!

Drums are quiet
Drums are loud
Especially when there are big crowds
Bing, bong, bing, bong!

Danny Sawyer (10)
Normandy Primary School

THE GREAT OAK TREE

The great oak tree
Is covered in bright acorns
The grass sways in the wind
We all must run towards it
And stand underneath.

Toni-Marie Chambers (10)
Normandy Primary School

MY VALENTINE

The boy I saw walking around
The boy I saw boogieing on down
The boy I saw with the handsome face
The boy I saw picking on Grace
This boy I saw who is the best
And better than the rest
The boy I saw who will stick up for me
The boy I saw who is big and strong
Where is the boy I saw?
I saw?

Samantha Challinor (10)
Normandy Primary School

GIRL TEACHERS

My teacher is sometimes nice,
Sometimes she just goes bad.
She puts on lots of make-up,
Boys think she's mad.

She likes to impress the boys,
So they all ask her out,
She likes them all,
There's no doubt!

She likes to go out at night,
She likes to dance and diva
She goes about half-past nine,
Singing, 'Night fever, night fever!'

Jade Blundell (10)
Normandy Primary School

THE WITCH'S KITCHEN

Inside the witch's kitchen in the corner of the room
Is a broom with a hard set of twigs.
In the middle of the room is a bubbling cauldron
That smells very horrible and is leaking.
On the shelf are some glasses saying 'Frogs' eyes' and 'Eyeballs'.
There's a black cat in the middle of the room purring.
Oh no, here comes the witch!
She's got me!
I'm a frog!

Sam Foster (10)
Normandy Primary School

FLOATING IN THE AIR

I fly my paper aeroplane to the land above,
I am waiting but no return,
I am still waiting.
Now it's time for bed.
Mum starts waiting,
So I go inside.
The next day comes,
I go outside,
I see my aeroplane,
I'm under my aeroplane
And I see,
Space!

Victoria Clark (9)
Normandy Primary School

SIMILE POEM

A rainbow is like different coloured glitter
    stuck up in the sky.
A rainbow is like glittery ink
    sprinkled across the sky.
A rainbow is like different coloured skittles
    stuck up in the sky.
A rainbow is like different flavoured ice cream
    that's been taken out of the fridge.
A rainbow is like a big coloured lollipop
    curling over the Earth.
A rainbow is like different coloured clouds
    spread across the sky.

Rachel Osborne (9)
Normandy Primary School

SNOW

Snow is like . . .
  sugar falling from the sky and covering the land.
Snow is like . . .
  Santa's beard covering all the ground.
Snow is like . . .
  flying cotton wool going round the sky.
Snow is like . . .
  icing from a giant's cake.
Snow is like . . .
  pillow feathers falling from the sky.
Snow is like . . .
  milk being poured over the Earth.

                    Snow is fun to play in
                    during the wintertime.

Hollie Reeve (9)
Normandy Primary School

FIREWORKS GO OFF

Fireworks go off in all different colours with a bang!
They're nice and bright, nice to watch
With loud pops and bangs
Babies are crying
Children are screaming
Dogs and cats are all hiding
All the adults are going, *'Ooh, ahh!'*
All the daddies are helping to set off the fireworks.
It's getting very scary!
Bang! Bang!
Sorry, there are no more fireworks left, so I've got to go,
Bye!

Sam Gardiner (10)
Normandy Primary School

SNOW

Snow is white stardust falling
               from Heaven.
Snow is a piece of cauliflower
               just put in a mouth.
Snow is a sheep's coat
               covering the land.
Snow is white daisies
               spread over the grass

Ronni Smart (9)
Normandy Primary School

VALENTINE ROSES

Roses are as red as blood,
Your heart contains love
And always will contain love,
You will always have an admirer,
You will always be together,
Forever and ever.

Natalie Floyd (9)
Normandy Primary School

ME IN MY BRAIN AND THE BLITZ FROM HELL!

I see me
in my brain
trying to kill
another person
Don't let
me

I
have to,   of
course,   it
is my   job
I came   to
fight war
not to be
scared!

I've
shot him
now. An
innocent
person. It
is my job
to fight
not to be   scared!

Eloise Barrett (10)
Normandy Primary School

THE TIGER

A tiger prances round and round,
hunting for its food,
It chases deer
And when it gets them, they are completely gone.

A tiger has stripes
And a tiger has spots,
Its eyes are like dots
And its body is yellow.

Jamie Smith (9)
Normandy Primary School

QUEEN ELIZABETH'S CUPBOARD IS LIKE...

Queen Elizabeth's cupboard is like a giant jewel,
Shaped into a cupboard for our Queen.
Queen Elizabeth's cupboard is like the queen of all cupboards,
Being filled with fabulous clothes.
Queen Elizabeth's cupboard is like a monster,
Gobbling up all the Queen's clothes.
Queen Elizabeth's cupboard is like a teacher,
Teaching the clothes to act ladylike.
Queen Elizabeth's cupboard is like a shopkeeper,
Selling clothes for Her Majesty.
Queen Elizabeth's cupboard is like a home,
For the people who need help.
Queen Elizabeth's cupboard is really a home for monsters,
So children, beware!

Francesca Bradford
Normandy Primary School

THE WITCH'S KITCHEN

A black battered base of an ancient cauldron
lingers in the corner lathered with old green waxy potion.
A mass of midsummer flowers, dead - it's winter now
and they're old, drooping and tired.

Certificates of witchcraft hang limply on the tarnished wall,
framed by splintered, rotten oak frames.

A tint shines on the dusty window giving not fresh,
but murky sunlight.

Emilia Jewitt (8)
St John's CE Primary School, Tunbridge Wells

SPLASHING AROUND!

What I like best
Is diving deep down,
Not walking, not running,
But swimming around,
Not skipping, not jumping,
Not sleeping, not grumping,
Messing about,
Without a doubt.
What I like best,
Swimming away, away,
Until the next day!

Rachel Tysh & Hannah Day (8)
St John's CE Primary School, Tunbridge Wells

THE WITCH'S KITCHEN

Dark gloomy place of spells and magic
A slimy, spooky and smoky cauldron sits in the corner.
Purple smoke coils and gives a sickly smell of evil
                                    to the revolting room.
Endless jars of poison are balanced on a red-capped toadstool.
The dust of grated frogs' heads fills the room.
Endless jars of poison sit above the cauldron.
Fragile cobwebs are on the ceiling.
Broken, battered brooms sag in a corner.
Witch wands hang on a wall, waiting to work the witch's
                                    wicked will once more.

Louise R Robinson (8)
St John's CE Primary School, Tunbridge Wells

THE FORGOTTEN FARMER'S BARN

Enter this place, and lose the smile on your face.
The compost whiff in this smelly, old, metal, rusty barn
Is from the old bundles of yarn.

In the corner stands a dark water pump,
A silent drip hangs and one day the pump will stop.

Clanging horseshoes, hard and rusty,
Swinging this way and that in the harsh wind.
Cow rings clattering in the tractor's trailer,
A faded fuchsia colour.

A slash of sunshine coming through a crack
In a willow wall.
Chicken feathers cluttering together
Like a white pillow, feathers so soft.

Mice scutter on their paws,
Like caterpillars on a leafy floor.
An ancient tyre, dusty-black,
Hanging on a bent hook.

The barn is a creepy place
And an utter disgrace!

Jack Kelehar & Charlotte Adams (8)
St John's CE Primary School, Tunbridge Wells

SWIMMING OUT WITH SCHOOL

Swimming out with school
Is the best lesson of all,
Doing the front crawl
Is the biggest problem of all.

Breaststroke
Backstroke
Float broke
She pokes!

Children dive
With a great splash!
Others arrive
With a big crash!

Then the end of the lesson comes
And there are the mums,
Dads, brothers, sisters,
Teenagers chewing gum.
The end of the lesson begins.
Poor things!

Gemma Bailey (9)
St John's CE Primary School, Tunbridge Wells

THE EXPLORER'S ATTIC

Torn, ancient maps are piled in corners.

There are no sounds except the falcon clock all day long,
Repeating tick-tock, tick-tock.

The knives are stabbed into a tree.
They are dirty, nothing but the reek of mud can be smelt.

Flippers scattered around and you can hardly walk,
In fact you always fall over.

Great statue of binoculars hung with his own, cluttered on top.

The explorer never cleans his old things.
He just stands there . . . day after day staring at his belongings.
He never gives them to charities, fêtes, jumble sales or auctions,
He just stands there.
For hours he stares at his snorkels - for this is where he keeps them,
Old, dark, black, broken, cracked snorkels.

Kieran Guy (8)
St John's CE Primary School, Tunbridge Wells

THE INVENTOR'S WORKSHOP

The inventor's workshop is filled to the top
with tired old inventions.
The gathercalanium droops down low
while the kisby hangs up high.
Old books, with torn-out pages.
Cobwebs covering the dusty covers.
Ancient tools not been used for years.
It's pitch-black in the inventor's workshop.
Only a single bat swoops through the thick air.
Dust-covered floors,
rats scurrying in and out of the broken door.
The woodwork is old and pitted.
A terrible whiff snakes around the room.
An old, musty, dirty smell.
Inventions are so rusty,
old books so musty.
There are potions filled with the most peculiar liquids.
All is quiet in the inventor's workshop,
for no one invents in there anymore.

Elliot Gathercole (9)
St John's CE Primary School, Tunbridge Wells

DOWN IN THE GOBLIN'S CELLAR

Down in the goblins cellar it smells of rotten eggs,
with a faint scent of blood dripping down human legs.
Down in the goblin's cellar it's grubby as can be,
with glimmering armour the rats can play in with glee.
Down in the goblin's cellar the walls ooze with slimy gunge,
but beware, step on the trapdoor and you're going for a plunge!
Don't go down to the goblin's cellar for anyone who has been
down there,
has suddenly died, and has been chucked out with the tide.

Jamie Taylor (9)
St John's CE Primary School, Tunbridge Wells

THE MONSTER'S CAVE

In the monster's cave
you'll have to be brave.
Eyes of old, stunned, brave humans line the floor
and every pace you take, you see more and more.
If you go there, you will not like it
because it will be like being in a black pit.
The walls are lumpy, slimy and green
but there is still much more you haven't seen.
Ancient pots floating in the air
the place is truly the monster's lair.
Gargantuan spiders and fragile cobwebs line the walls
on and on until the dinosaur calls.
The smell is nauseating, unbreathable and sickening
this is the time you feel like chickening.
There are also dead humans with terror in their eyes
you start to flee from where the monster lies.

Henry Walsgrove (8)
St John's CE Primary School, Tunbridge Wells

THE EXPLORER'S ATTIC

The explorer's attic is very new
There are no sounds
except the moo
of the antique cow clock
but who is the explorer?

He has beautiful boots
and fur-striped suits,
A splintered axe
and a medieval rucksack
but who is the explorer?

There's a murderous machete
and a blue settee.
There's a shiny penknife
but his life is at stake.
So we shall say farewell
as he drops to Hell
But we don't know
He might go to Heaven.
But who is the explorer?

Well I can tell you that the explorer is
Andrew,
because I knew it wasn't you
because you don't have a . . .
murderous machete
medieval rucksack
antique cow clock
beautiful boots
splintered axe
blue settee
shiny penknife
and you . . .
    don't have the whiffing smell of old things
or do you?

Alistair Hookway (9)
St John's CE Primary School, Tunbridge Wells

SUPER SPLASHING

Super splashing,
People clashing,
People playing games,
Water down the drains,
Splash! Water makes it rain.
Messing about,
Without a doubt,
Someone will shout:
Get out!

Kieran Guy & Andrew Wilson (9)
St John's CE Primary School, Tunbridge Wells

SNAKE

Tightly coiled and fast asleep
His fangs and venom buried deep.
No movement from his patterned back
Dreaming of his prey and attack.
Hissss! Suddenly the scales unslither.
I think that he must have smelt his dinner!

Sam Barnes (9)
St John's CE Primary School, Tunbridge Wells

THE GRASS SNAKE!

He wriggles and squirms along the grass,
He hisses along the way to find his prey.
His big bulging eyes gleaming in the sun.
No one can see him, his prey on the run!

Louise Beasley (10)
St John's CE Primary School, Tunbridge Wells

THE SLOW HEDGEHOG

Max, the hedgehog,
Short and slow,
Black and brown,
Liked eating maggots all day long.

One fine night,
Full of stars,
Warm and dry,
He thought it was a perfect time to walk.

He wanted to go to the park,
Green and big,
With a large lake,
Which was down the hill.

His way to travel,
Curled up in a ball,
Rolling full speed,
Brought the hedgehog quickly to the feast.

Samantha McCall (9)
St John's CE Primary School, Tunbridge Wells

THE ATTIC

I see broken black lamps,
Paintings of my family,
A grandfather clock that has stopped,
There are no sounds in the attic.

The old chest that has rusty locks,
A recording of sheep in flocks,
A grandfather clock that has stopped,
There are no sounds in the attic.

A beehive with no bees,
Old maths books that nobody sees,
A grandfather clock that has stopped,
There are no sounds in the attic.

I love my attic,
I love shutting the door
And sitting in the wooden rocking chair
That has seen me before,
And listening for sounds in the attic.

Amy Fraser (8) & Andrew Hillocks (9)
St John's CE Primary School, Tunbridge Wells

THE ATTIC

When I'm allowed in the attic
I always feel very proud,
There's a graduation hat with tassels
One my mum once wore
And ivory tusks inherited from Father's family bore.

There are tennis racquets with broken strings,
A snapped guitar among other things.
Old popular Lego, long since forgotten
And now drowned in dust,
And a lonely old teddy who's missing some fluff.

When I'm alone in the attic,
I play with Mum's old wooden doll's house
And when I'm there a small field mouse
Comes to stay and play,
When I'm alone in the attic.

Henry Reynolds (9)
St John's CE Primary School, Tunbridge Wells

WINTER

Winter's face is livid with rage,
His hair is a hoary frost,
His merciless eyes are filled with hatred,
His teeth and fingers are icicles as sharp as knives.

Winter has a polar cloak,
He has a crown of ice and holly,
He has the robes of the Arctic.

Winter is mean and spiteful,
He tears across the sky in his silver chariot,
Drawn by pure white horses,
He leaves the world carpeted in pure white snow,
Cheerless people trudge along deserted streets.

Winter is dawning.

Thomas Engleback (10)
St John's CE Primary School, Tunbridge Wells

MY FIRST DAY AT SCHOOL

New shoes, shiny and blue
stiff shirt, crisp skirt.
Little legs can't reach the name peg
wobbly wave, trying to be brave.
Sitting cross-legged on the floor
feeling very raw.
The giant teacher is a smiley creature
she reads aloud while I watch the clouds.
Then my name gives me fame.
Reading writing, drawing exploring,
bells and smells, time for lunch.
Big benches, dangly feet,
time to eat my chocolate treat.
Time to run in the sun.
It's afternoon, Mum's coming soon.
Feeling tired, nearly expired.
End of day, no time to stay.

Rosemarie Crouch (10)
St John's CE Primary School, Tunbridge Wells

I CAN'T BELIEVE . . .

The cricket player bought a flying bat.
The tennis player went on the net.
The magician played football and he scored a hat-trick.
The scientist kept fit by physical exercise.
The fashion designer was in a fit.
The baseball player kept catching the girls' attention.

What strange things I have heard,
But who told me? A little bird!

Sam Patterson (10)
St John's CE Primary School, Tunbridge Wells

HAPPINESS

Happiness, the bride of love,
Sits peacefully.
Bliss filling all her thoughts.
She dances with joy,
Leaps with mirth.
Her embrace brings felicity,
Her kiss spreads jubilation.
She wears a jade-green dress so beautiful,
You smile.
Hair so orange and silky,
You touch.
Sky-blue shoes so wonderful,
You try them on
And find yourself in a place of
Eternal delight.

Lizzie Fraser (10)
St John's CE Primary School, Tunbridge Wells

WINTER

The Queen of Winter rushes in, brushing autumn away,
Blowing away the warmth of summer.
Her hair frosted silver and her fingernails, icicles,
She slinks along in her gown of snow.
Her pale face with deep blue eyes,
On her feet, ice-glass slippers.
Her lips as red as holly berries,
Her body tall and slender like a bare tree.
What mood will she be in today?
Will she be angry causing storms, thunder and lightning?
Will she be sad, crying tears of rain?
Will she be happy, making clear blue skies and snowball fights?
Will she blow steamy breath creating misty fog?
She could create so many things,
Thaw, rain, frost, gale - all these things she controls.
As winter's turn draws to a close,
Her elderly grasp begins to weaken
As spring rushes in.

Helen Robinson (11)
St John's CE Primary School, Tunbridge Wells

OCEAN

Dressed in a blue flowing gown,
With long, grey, wavy hair
And vibrant, deep blue eyes,
Her shoes made of the finest seaweed.

At night she gazes up at the stars
And wishes she was up there too,
In the daytime she sees children happily building sandcastles
on the beach
And seagulls in the sky.

Anger floods over her as the storm thunders in the dark sky,
Her ripples turn to huge waves which flood the beaches and send
everyone home,
Every time she tries to calm down,
The wind and rain urge her on.

Speedboats often roar through her and send waves cascading
over her dress,
Which makes her very angry,
People swim in the shallow arches of her feet
And minnows dart between her toes.

Jessica Martin (11)
St John's CE Primary School, Tunbridge Wells

SPRING

She creeps up behind Winter, quiet and stealthy, like a mouse,
as powerful as a lion, but clothed in a gown of green and blue.
'Boo!' she yells, slapping him on the back of the head with such
huge force that he comes crashing to the ground.
Winter, completely lost for words, flees into the woods to conserve
his snow for next year.
Then, with one swish of her gown, the whole world becomes a ray
of colours,
The sky, an ocean shade of blue, the grass, an emerald shade of green.
The bushes grow rosy buds, like those on top of her golden crown.
She strides over to her throne of bushes to have a rest,
Only to be chased away by Mother Summer in her turn.

George Walsgrove (10)
St John's CE Primary School, Tunbridge Wells

THE MUMMY'S TOMB

In the darkened tomb
The sarcophagus of glinting gold,
Sits in the corner, dusty,
Waiting to be found,
The golden chest,
Just waiting to be found,
Untouched for centuries past
Waiting to be found.
Fat spiders sit in dusty, fragile webs,
Some hanging . . . dead!
Millenniums have passed
Nothing!
No robbers found this jewelled case.
The mummy's mystery
Yet to be unravelled.

Samuel Jones (9)
St John's CE Primary School, Tunbridge Wells

THE DRAGON'S LAIR

In there, in there,
The dragon's lair,
The dim lights
From the fire torches,
Flaming in the night.
The dragon launches,
Leaving the grimy walls
And the slimy floors
Of its cave.

The dragon returns
Sharpening its claws,
On grey scarred walls,
Slavering, champing
Its powerful jaws,
Turning its greedy gaze
On the bright indented armour,
Chained to the bone-strewn floor,
The ceiling beaded
With fiery red blood.
The strong smell
Of burnt material
Fills the room,
The rustling dragon scales
Squeezing through
The narrow entrance,
And the mysterious sound
Of bones clicking together.

Helena Vallely (8)
St John's CE Primary School, Tunbridge Wells

THE INVENTOR'S ATTIC

Professor Prewit is long gone now,
But his proud inventions still remain.
The musty time machine still whirrs, desperately trying to keep alive,
But one day it, too, will splutter and cough to silence.
The lingering smell of old tobacco smoke
Still hangs in the air.
His old travel journal and globe lie forgotten in a corner.

A breeze rustles the pages of study books,
Blowing through the open window.
His three-legged table stands splintered and chipped
On creaking hinges.
His old creaking sofa wobbles on rickety legs.
Professor Prewit's mechanical tools hang ancient,
Silent and unreproachful,
On the cold damp walls of the attic.

Jonathan Walter (8)
St John's CE Primary School, Tunbridge Wells

SPRING!

Spring is here!
Winter's cold months
Have blown by now,
As the birds fly north.

Fairy gold blooms everywhere,
Daffodils, daisies and lilies.
The sun is happy once more,
Golden on the melting snow.

Spring dances through the trees,
Singing at the top of her voice.
Colouring the ground,
Grass-green beneath her.

Squirrels dance out,
From their nests above.
The lambs in the meadow,
Coming into a new world of spring!

Arnesta Odone
St John's CE Primary School, Tunbridge Wells

WINTER AND SPRING

The air is bitter and frosty,
The windows covered with silver splinters,
Rivers and streams are frozen.
Winter tiptoes along the snow,
Careful not to wake the flowers and creatures under their duvets,
Wearing her tiara of icicles and swathed in a long white gown,
Her silver shoes shimmer as the bleak sun peeps out through
the cold, grey, lifeless sky.
Winter panics, Spring has come.
Spring sweeps along the path towards Winter,
Her pea-green dress fluttering in the wind.
Behind, the world is full of colours, red, green, gold, yellow, blue
and orange.
Winter suddenly feels it, a warm breeze seeping through her skin,
The snow, Winter's snow, melting her tiara, trickling down her face.
She trips and falls, her white dress now dirt-brown.
Spring smiles sweetly as her dress swipes the forehead of Winter,
She snatches away Winter and the world is colourful again.
Now it is spring, glorious spring.

Catherine Children (11)
St John's CE Primary School, Tunbridge Wells

JOY

Wrapped in a glimmering coat of silk, she ambles through the
                                                    pine-green forest.
I hear her chuckling quietly to herself as she feels the fresh air.
She watches the children singing and dancing gladly,
Whispering for them to come and join her in happiness.
When she is around, the flowers bloom bright colours of
                                                    violet and amber.
Dancing delicately through the air, she smiles,
Twisting, turning, her tiny feet hardly touching the ground.
Feeling the cool breeze rush through her hair,
She grins at the sun and at the world around her,
Overhearing the captivating sounds of the birds singing.
She glimpses all the happy faces.
As the day comes to an end, leaving behind a trail of gladness,
She sneaks off into her bed of golden-yellow
Under a duvet of smooth, shiny petals,
Resting her delicate head on a pillow of shimmering leaves.

Rebecca Stephens (10)
St John's CE Primary School, Tunbridge Wells

VOLCANO!

He lives in a dark, gloomy land,
Swelling anger building inside.
We dare not enter his foul territory,
For fear we will be prey.

Bubble, bubble, rumble, rumble.

His misty dark hair coils around him,
His grouchy frown striking fear in all.
None can change his dreadful plan,
Spilling rage burning red-hot fury.

Bubble, bubble, rumble, rumble.

Our screaming cries ringing,
Black lakes of lava pouring in our direction,
Our little village in its way,
Screaming, then silence!

Sleep deep sleep.

Abigail Clarke (10)
St John's CE Primary School, Tunbridge Wells

ANGER

Anger drifts through the sun-dappled thicket,
Livid with hate and putrid with rage.
He rambles through tree after tree, their leaves knotted
and with spiral branches.
He gathers his friends and companions and
whispers strange words.
He wreaks havoc among all who stand in his way.
He wears a coat of fire and a crown of needle-sharp thorns.
He loathes all happiness and joy.
His breath, as hot as mercury and as poisonous as venom.

Anger, the Devil's nephew!

Georgie Gray (10)
St John's CE Primary School, Tunbridge Wells

AUTUMN

Her carmine garments sweep down to her diminutive feet,
She makes no sound as she treks in-between her titanic creations,
The leaves cover her with confetti,
The branches bow at her feet.
They all perform for Autumn,
Dancing and swaying on a high stage to win her approval.

But Autumn pays no attention to them,
She commands all the leaves to fall and shrivel,
Because Autumn despises Spring.

To finish her glorious scheme,
She invites Winter to stay for four elongated months,
For Autumn knows what Winter brings,
Frost, snow and cold,
Which makes the flowers die,
The leaves get frostbite.

Autumn is happy as she rushes away,
Leaving Winter to do his worst,
Murdering, annihilating.
More work for Spring to do,
Winter kills all her creations,
Which were created nearly a year ago.

Elizabeth Robertson (11)
St John's CE Primary School, Tunbridge Wells

ROYAL WINTER

Across the icy floor, the King and Queen of Winter dance together
arm in arm.
They kiss, they kiss, and it changes everything.
A freeze quivers down their spines.
They stare at each other with chilled eyes.
Not with embarrassment but with fear.
They stray to opposite sides of the icy ballroom.
King skates off into the green, pinewood, glassy forest
leaving behind a shiny silver trail.
Tears cascade down Queen's frozen cheeks and burn
her silky white skin.
She skates towards him, lunges out for him, reaches, but falls with
her hands clutched close to her chest.
But Spring has come and the aged Winter has passed.
Now it is time for the heat of the sun; the fiery ball in the sky
that sucks her in.
She falls to the ballroom floor as the scorching sun beats down on her
frozen dress and melts her into clear water.
Now she has to wait a year till her time comes around again.

Kiri Rayner (10)
St John's CE Primary School, Tunbridge Wells

ANGER

A young maiden with flaming red hair,
Bloodshot eyes and a devilish snare,
A blazing dress, hot to the touch
And the stompy attitude
Happiness hates so much.

Her steamy nose and stampy feet,
Joy and Happiness playing ball,
But when Anger comes they have to retreat,
She leaves behind a gust of red smoke,
Which makes Love stop and choke.

She is the servant of the Fire Queen,
With her partners, Fear, Jealousy,
Hatred, Violence and Hostility,
All as mean as she - as mean, as mean as can be!

Leah Breckman (10)
St John's CE Primary School, Tunbridge Wells

ANGER

The morning sky has lit up the world.
Anger's around with fury on his face.
He's never happy, he's always angry.
Anger makes the sky go red, crimson-red.
His fiery footsteps glow bright red in the terrifying dark.
As Anger walks in the hazy day,
Leaves and nature all die.
Anger is caged up with fury
In the disintegrating world.
Anger has no friends
Because he is a fiend.
He loathes everybody in sight.
Anger never dies!

Tristan Lenczner (11)
St John's CE Primary School, Tunbridge Wells

ANGER

She dances over boiling lava,
In a sizzling dress of fire,
Gashing people with clawed fingers,
In her livid rage.
Screaming in the night,
Waking the riders in black,
They hear her song.
Her evil, her pure evil,
Spinning in people's minds,
Rotting all their heavenly achievements,
Producing acrimonious creatures,
With the eye of fire that rules over all the land,
Remember, she'll endlessly be watching you!

Amelia Fedrick (10)
St John's CE Primary School, Tunbridge Wells

HAPPINESS!

Happiness loves to play.
As she hides for you to seek, her long, fair hair flows behind her.
She will skip and prance all the way to her hiding place.
Her brothers, Temper and Anger,
The twins, constantly endeavour to get in her way.
Happiness has tools for getting past her brothers:
A smile or giggle, maybe a laugh.
She is the most beautiful of all her family.
Her elegant dance puts humans in a trance of joy.
All can catch her smile.
Radiant as an angel, she is always glowing brightly.
Calming blue eyes see into your mind and her dress leaves
A trail of laughter.
Soft hands touch your face.
Eternally awake, she gives good dreams, a slight smile on faces.
No matter how hard it is to find her, you always can -
Just follow her trail of laughter.

Aimie Constable (11)
St John's CE Primary School, Tunbridge Wells

AND MY HEART SOARS

The floating of the leaves,
The softness of the air,
The redness of the glittering roses,
Speak to me.

The sparkles of the life around,
The fastness of the cars going by,
The description of the books,
Speak to me.

The brightness of the sun,
The thunder in the sky,
The swaying of the dark green grass,
Speak to me.

The hardness of the ground,
The bobbing of a boat,
The wet dark ink of pens
And the life that never goes away,
They speak to me.

And my heart soars!

Christopher Deakins (8)
St Katharine's CP School, Knockholt

THE MOUNTAINS

It stretches to the heavens
And the skies above
The white on the top
Looks like a dove.

Mountain climbers
They take a risk
Not doing it slow
Or doing it brisk.

When climbing a mountain
Take great care
But if you don't
Beware!

Joe Tarbert (8)
St Katharine's CP School, Knockholt

JET PLANE

Faster than sound
But slower than light.
It's like a fly with weaponry
Or a ball hit out of sight.
Its engine roars
Like a tiger.
Machine guns go
Rat-a-tat-tat
Like a stick on a bat.
It lands like
A duck on a pond.
It's a metal bird.
It's a flying computer.
It's a bird
With engines.
It's a flying rocket.
It's a jet plane!

Alexander Deakins (11)
St Katharine's CP School, Knockholt

MY HAMSTER

My hamster is soft as a teddy bear
Her face is gentle as a puppy
Her teeth are sharp as razor blades
She has the most amazing ginger fur
Her eyes are as big as blackberries
Her nose tickles my ear like a feather
Her fur coat is warm as a blanket
She sleeps soundly as a mouse!

Roberta Stephens (9)
St Katharine's CP School, Knockholt

MY FRIEND

My friend is
Like the wind
Making the grass dance happily.

My friend is
Like a blanket
Keeping me warm through the night.

My friend is
Like a dove
Soaring through the sky.

My friend
Is like a mountain
Tall, tough and strong.

Grace Dowley (10)
St Katharine's CP School, Knockholt

MY FRIEND

My friend always
Laughs
When I say a joke, I feel comforted

When she is
Excited, she
Can always cool down.

When she is
down, she is
Easily cheered up.

Her voice
Is always full
Of nice things.

She is
my friend
And I
Am hers.

Rosie Hodson (11)
St Katharine's CP School, Knockholt

MY FRIEND

My friend is
Like fire,
Warming up the cold, starry night.

She is
Like a soft, fluffy pillow,
Comforting the most uncomfortable person.

Her friendly smile is
Rarer than a unicorn.

Her laughter is like
An audience,
Laughing at a really funny circus.

She is my friend
And I am hers.

Michael Turner (9)
St Katharine's CP School, Knockholt

LOOKING THROUGH THE EYE OF LONDON

Skyscrapers like needles poking through the sky
People like ants walking around hurriedly
Cars like multicoloured beetles
Bridges like harps creaking under their weight
Scaffolding, tiny stairs reaching up to the rooftops
The Thames, a little spill from God's house
The Dome, a huge cake with cheese strings going through it.
Modern buildings, just landed there, spaceships from outer space.

Freddie Barr-Smith (10)
St Katharine's CP School, Knockholt

GOING SWIMMING

The sun shines down on the water making it look like a mirror.
The water is as smooth as ice
And as warm as a bath.
I gently glide through the water like a dolphin.
The water covers me like a tidal wave.
The water is an *angry* whale
Spurting water everywhere
The water
Ripples over me like a snake's body.

Charlotte Rogers (10)
St Katharine's CP School, Knockholt

SKIING

The air flies by as I rush down the hill
Other skiers going as slow as snails
Flying down as fast as a rock to the moon
Then comes the mistake like a bird hitting a tree
Instead of going downhill I fly in the air
Impact, like a stone hitting the floor
Freezing snow hits my face
The taste of snow
It is as cold as ice
I carry on going as the snails overtake me
I am last
I am as slow as them
I feel like an ice cube
At home I toast my feet
Like bread in a toaster
I feel as warm as fire.

Sam Taylor (10)
St Katharine's CP School, Knockholt

MY HAMSTER SPEEDO

My hamster Speedo,
Is as fast as fast can be.
Scampering around the cage like a fly in a box.
Holding onto the top of his cage like a helicopter.
Charging through his tube like a tube train.
He is a Batman hamster.
Racing from house to wheel like a racing car.
He is a mini-hamster athlete.
Fast as a car.
Spinning his wheel like a speeding Ferris wheel.
Wild as a bull.
Crazy as a spooked horse.

Matthew Nightingale (10)
St Katharine's CP School, Knockholt

MY DOG RUFUS

When Rufus and I are alone in a room, I sit on the floor with him
lying next to me.
I then tell him all about my day and he listens to every single word
that comes out of my mouth.
When we take him for a walk in the field he prances around
because he is enjoying himself so much.
When I open the kitchen door to say hello to him he jumps on top
of me and tries to lick me.

My dog Rufus is a fiery flame bolting around and round
the garden.
He is a little angel always ready to greet me when
I arrive home.
Dogs are just like humans, they can love and care
for each other.
Rufus can occasionally become an angry bear when told off.
He has a huge mane and is the king of the jungle.
He is a guard dog, not letting a single stranger set foot
in our house.
He is a child, always wanting to be loved and tickled.
He is a lively big cat running around wildly.

Sadie Pitman (11)
St Katharine's CP School, Knockholt

THE MOON

One great big glowing eye lighting up the darkness.
Its body camouflaged in the surrounding gloom.
The eyelid closes on the eye sideways, so slowly and carefully
You think it would stop altogether.
But it is always there, even if we can't see it.
It moves around the Earth as though trying to find a comfy spot,
In-between the planets.
But it never makes a sound.

Madeleine Flawn (9)
Shipbourne School

MY BROTHER

He can't get any better,
He's already the best,
Only at one thing,
Hitting me in the chest.
He is very brave
And really tough,
With Harry Potter,
He's in Hufflepuff.
He watches TV
All the time,
But I hope
He likes this rhyme.
He is really smart
And ever so cool,
The only thing that's wrong
Is he hates school.
His name is Adam,
The best name ever
And . . .
We get along together.

Sadie Smurthwaite (9)
Upton Primary School

MY DOG RUDY

My dog Rudy is big and grey,
He likes to run, he likes to play,
When it snows he pulls my sleigh,
My dog Rudy is big and grey.
My dog Rudy is big and tough,
His bark is loud and very gruff,
My dog Rudy's the dog I love.

Amy Stuchbery (8)
Upton Primary School

Once I Saw A Butterfly

Once I saw a butterfly
That fluttered high in the sky
My, oh my, what a butterfly!

Rebecca Kirwan (8)
Upton Primary School

OWLS

Owls, wise old owls,
Sitting upon the midnight tree,
Watching ahead of deep moonlight,
Looking for delicate prey.

Fly off into the moonlit sky
Stop off on a wobbling branch
To eat a scrumptious white mouse
'Yum, yum, yum,'
Said the wise old owl.

Owls, wise old owls
Say it's time for a good night's sleep
'Night, night,' said the wise old owl.

Isabelle Richards (8)
Upton Primary School

DREAMS

At night-time when I go to bed
as soon as my pillow touches my head,
dreams come through to my brain
of a teddy dancing and a steaming train.

Flowers have opened and are nice and bright
while I sit and fly my kite,
children run and kick a ball
and then run into the hall.

At night-time when I go to bed
dreams just can't stop filling my head.

Georgia Hickman (11)
Upton Primary School

BLIZZARD

A blizzard was coming
people were running

We were watching the news
we all had the blues

We wrapped up warm
waiting for the snowstorm

Fluffy and white it fell
through the night

As morning was yawning
the snow was still falling

It fell in great flakes
we just wanted a break

It started to settle
we boiled the kettle

We prayed and prayed
but still it stayed.

Daniel Stuchbery (9)
Upton Primary School

TEACHERS

Teachers always say:
'Honesty's the best policy,'
but they lie about their age,
saying they're 21
when they're really 48.

Teachers always tell you off
in a really sarcastic way, like:
'Sorry, am I interrupting your
conversation, Kate?'
Honestly, give us a break!

Some teachers aren't so bad,
but others are plain mad,
rustling and bustling about,
nagging children to do their
homework on time.

Oops, looks like I forgot to do mine!

Rebecca Fairbank (9)
Upton Primary School

OUR WORST NIGHTMARE

Boys

A boy's worst nightmare must be girls,
Covered in make-up with hair full of curls,
Their jazzy skirts and clonky shoes,
With all their gossip and latest news,
The girls scattered with blusher and red rosy cheeks
And their girly perfume which really reeks,
Their long fair hair covered in lacquer,
With slobby lips ready to plant you with a huge juicy smacker!

Girls

A girl's worst nightmare must be boys,
Who always torment, who always annoy,
The boys who always gel up their hair
And at the end of the day they look like a bear,
Think they're all cool, think they can fight,
Believe they're 'it', know they're always right,
Always stick together, always take sides,
Can't take a joke and think we are taking them for a ride!

Danielle Willingale (10)
Upton Primary School

BORING SCHOOL

Boring school
work for all.
Circle time for a good time
and poems for a good rhyme.
PE and art's fun
and all the homework's done,
going to the computer room,
doing work on an Egyptian tomb.
Work on charts,
nursery have go-karts.
Competitions to win,
food in the bin,
a scraping chalk
and children talk,
maths test, English test,
play time's here so let's have a rest.
Football's good,
a story called Red Riding Hood.
Home time's here,
so let's have a cheer.

Sam Parker (8)
Upton Primary School

I WISH...

I wish I was a hamster
I'd eat and sleep and play
And if someone tried to pick me up
Then I would run away!

I wish I was a puppy
I'd run all over the park
And if the postman came to my house
Then I would *yap, growl, bark!*

I wish I was a kitten
I'd play with cotton wool
I'd always land on four feet
If I happened to fall!

Or I could be a dolphin
And dive down really deep
And when the tourists came along
Out of the water I'd leap!

Yet I could be a pony
And eat up all the hay
And I could go in my stable
If it was a rainy day!

All of those would be great
But I'll just have to be me
Though if I was an animal
I'd be a cheeky monkey!

Josie Carder (10)
Upton Primary School

MY DREAM

I once had a dream that I flew to the moon,
In a bright yellow rocket, the shape of a spoon.
When I arrived and stepped out of the ship,
I discovered an alien having a kip.
I crept past him silently so as not to wake,
His eyes slowly opened as my legs began to shake.
'Who are you?' he asked quite quick,
'I'm a human,' I replied in a tick.
Eventually he stood up and drew nearer to me,
I backed away very gingerly.
And there lay an egg about to crack,
And as it did, it began to attack.
Millions of aliens crept out of the eggs,
Each with about a billion legs.
I looked in amazement at their red staring eyes,
Wondering if they were astronauts dressed in disguise.
Suddenly I awoke with Mum calling, 'Get ready for school!'
And that was when I realised that my dream wasn't real at all!

Sarah Whelan (10)
Upton Primary School

THE RIVER

The river flows, glistening in the sun,
People wondering from where it had come,
Sticks would pass right by your eye,
Children watching as it goes by.

Dawn would come and it would start to glisten,
Animals would come near, just to listen
The water so cool and so fresh
Swans glide by effortless.

Every time it rains
People stare in vain.
The ripples run through the water
Carrying the ducks along, like a porter.

The night comes again as rabbits creep away,
There's only one animal that dares to stay,
The people sit by the river giving it a name,
The children playing by the river, their little game.

Hannah Wilks (10)
Upton Primary School

THE SPOOKY BALL

Tonight on Hallowe'en is the Spooky Ball,
Every witch an' ghoul will be in the Haunted Hall.
The skeletons play the trombones,
With mummies on the saxophones.

Tonight on Hallowe'en is the Spooky Ball,
There are centuries of coffins all around the wall,
All the vampires play the violins,
While ghosts snack on rotting fins.

Everyone avoids all the black cats' path,
And hope not to meet Count Dracula's wrath.
Witches and ghosts will scare you all,
After they've left the Spooky Ball.

Abigail Forsyth (10)
Upton Primary School

WHAT WILL I BE?

What will I be when I grow up?
I might be a footballer
And win some golden cups.
Maybe a dustman will suit me best;
Story writing is OK, but you never know,
I might be an annoying little pest.
A builder may be good,
I would be a famous spy,
But I doubt I could.
Here is a rubbish job, you see,
Work in a food shop,
That is a bit naff for me.
I might reach a chess master,
Or run on the tracks,
And get much faster.
Being an actor would be fun
I have always liked drama,
But I think I would prefer to run.
A train driver is what my uncle does,
I also know someone who does printing
With lots of machines, which always buzz.

I wouldn't say I must decide yet.
I've got a long time to go,
I must wait and think another day.

Ray Humm (10)
Upton Primary School

THE WHITE WORLD

The whirling of the snowflakes brush against my cheek
As I tread softly through the crunching snow.
The robins' calls are flattened by the gushing wind,
My soft crunching footsteps can barely be heard.
My feet are sinking, deeper, deeper, deeper,
The white world has come.
I bend down and pick up some powdery snow,
I roll it and take aim,
I see a boy who's just thrown a snowball at my friend,
Suddenly I reach up, bend my arm back and fling forward,
Direct hit!
The boy turns,
I run, run, run . . .!

Caitlin Maslen (9)
Upton Primary School

WHAT DAYS ARE HOT DAYS?

What days are hot days?

Different colours, flowers sprouting
Or lots of people going on outings.

What days are hot days?

Lots of different colours in the sky
Or your mummy making blackcurrant pie.

What days are hot days?

Is it lots of bugs around you
Or is it all the bugs that fly?

No, it's summer!

Josephine Wynne-Williams (9)
Upton Primary School

MY GREATEST FEARS

My greatest fears were coming true
I didn't think it would happen
It was worse than watching Sunday night news
I still didn't think it would happen.

Like tortoises strolling in a herd
We lined up for the breathtaking ride.
I was in front, it looked pitch-black
Then there was a startled thump.
We had started moving!

I was petrified
Then there was a huge drop.
My cheeks were being flattened by the rough wind.
I figured it was over so
I went to buy the photo
And I looked like a hangover.

Matthew Kent (10)
West Malling Primary School

MY DREAM

My dream
Is to be
A teacher
And teach a class
Of thirty children

It would be like
Teaching diamonds
Their times tables

I would feel like
I was being pulled
Into a world full of angels

My dream is to teach.

Damien Boyce (10)
West Malling Primary School

MY WORST FEAR

The roller coaster is
My worst fear of all.
It climbs and falls
Like a crashing wave.
My stomach tosses and turns,
Screams of excitement
Like a flock of babbling seagulls.

The speed as fast as Concorde
Zooming through the blue sky.
Flashes of colour
Like a never stopping traffic light.

I look forward to when it stops
Just like biting into
A delicious ice cream.

Joshua Penfold (9)
West Malling Primary School

MY FAVOURITE PET

My favourite pet is
My nan's old crazy dog.
Her fur is like
Soft cotton wool.
She barks
For no reason at all
And it sounds like
A steam train
Thundering along the railway track
On a foggy November night.

My favourite animal
Is my nan's dozy dog.
She lies on her back
Like a beetle struggling to turn over
On a blistering summer's day
On the golden lawn in the garden.

I love my nan's dog.

Lewis Utting (9)
West Malling Primary School

TAKE THE PLUNGE

Swimming is exciting like a child going to a circus
Cool water flowing in the rippling swimming pool
Colourful floats bobbing around like jellyfish, in the azure sea.

People diving like dolphins flying into the sunset
Laughing ecstatically like a pack of hyenas
The sun sparkling on the water like a million diamonds
Feeling as warm as a newborn egg in a feathery nest.

Samantha Beckett (9)
West Malling Primary School

MY FAVOURITE PET

My favourite pet
is my cat Tilly
who pats my hand like a tender newborn baby
crawling along the floor.

When I saunter past
she chases me upstairs like a famished stray dog
hunting for some food.

When I'm in my room
she leaps up onto my bed
then she miaows
and tries to get my attention
like a rowdy cow stampeding
because it's being chased.

Tilly is my favourite pet
because she is my best friend.
She plays with me as if she were still a kitten.

Jacob Williamson (10)
West Malling Primary School

PETRIFIED

Once, one petrifying night
A murky old cottage stood desolate
As sombre as a pyramid left to crumble down
As it only just survives
Its last days.

The trees had pointed branches
Like fingers
With their knuckles bending in all directions
On that terrifying night.

The rain was racing towards the ground
Like a tap turned all the way on
In an echoing room full of nothing but darkness.

Lightning crashed against the clouds
Crashing and smashing its way through
Its arms of light
Getting closer and closer to its destination.

The winds were rushing past
As if they were late
Swish, swoosh! Like wolves howling at the moon.

Waves pushing their way over the ocean
Creating a channel of their own
Like a car zooming through the Channel Tunnel
As fast as it could possibly go.

A girl rooted to the spot in her fright
As she looked over to the cemetery
Where the lightning and thunder crashed together
Like fireworks exploding in the sky.

These are the fears of the night
When all around you are petrified.

Madeleine Atkins (10)
West Malling Primary School

A GHOST?

Walking along the dark alleyway
the trees and bushes begin to sway
you could hear a pin drop down
I stop and stare then turn around.

Then as I walk along the street
something creeps beneath my feet
the gloomy campsite has no tent
now the tension is very tense.

The wind starts to blow and howl
like a wolf starting its prowl
I'm going in the deep dark wood
being punished for not being good.

As I say my last words
a vague figure appears
who is that scary-looking nutter?
Phew, it's only Iain, my brother.

Kate Lucey (9)
West Malling Primary School

THE STORM

The trees swaying to and fro
As if their roots were magnetic
And the force was too strong for them to let go.

The wind howling and swooshing
Through the town
As if it were the wind's worst enemy.

The waves crashing on the sandbank
Like icing flooding over the cake
As I slowly tip the jar.

The children transfixed in their fear
As if they were engrossed
In a really funny programme.

The owls hooting in the black night
As if they were calling their friends
Because they were lost.

The storm was petrifying
In its rage!

Annalisa Bevans (9)
West Malling Primary School